Printed and Published in Great Britain by D. C. THOMSON & CO., LTD.,
185 Fleet Street, London EC4A 2HS.
© D. C. THOMSON & CO., LTD., 1983.
ISBN 0 85116 271 1

Pool disaster—man in plaster!

Upset by a pet!

Fancy that—a swimming cat!

GNASHER'S TALE

I say! I say!—The ground's given way!

SMUDGE

THE BOY WHO'D LOVE TO SEE SNOW BLACK AS BLACK CAN BE!

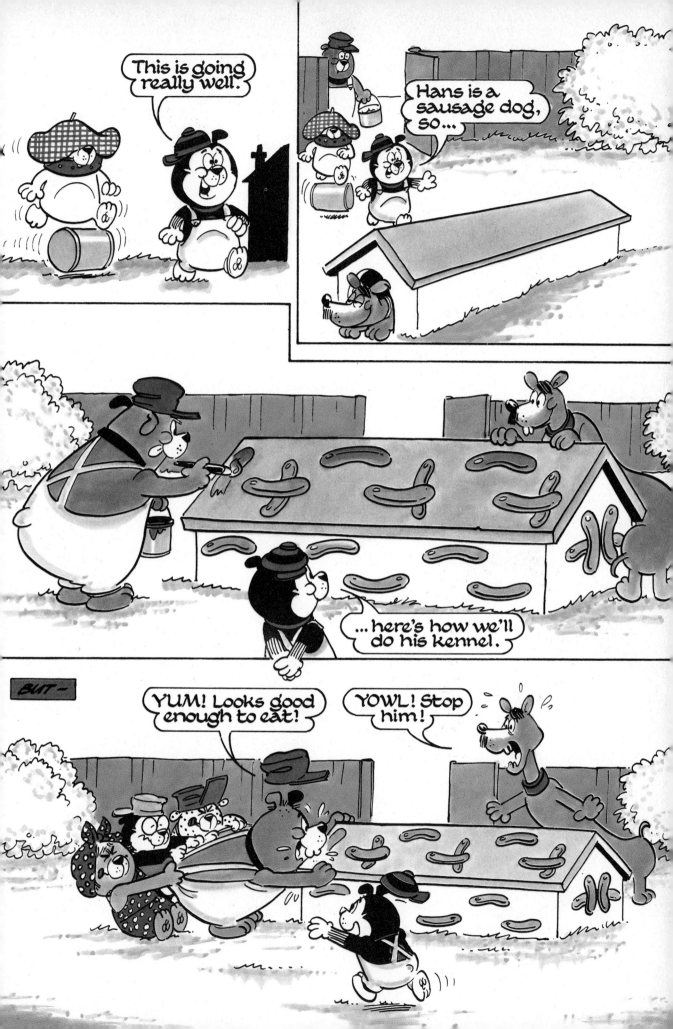

What um fright on Chiefy's bath night!

Snowball fight at a great height!

His loaf's destroyed—is Dad annoyed?

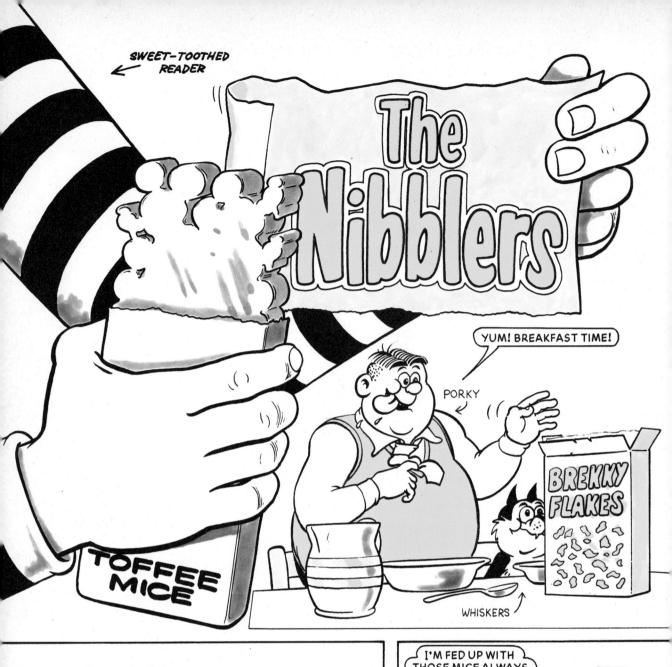

What hard luck—plan's come unstuck!

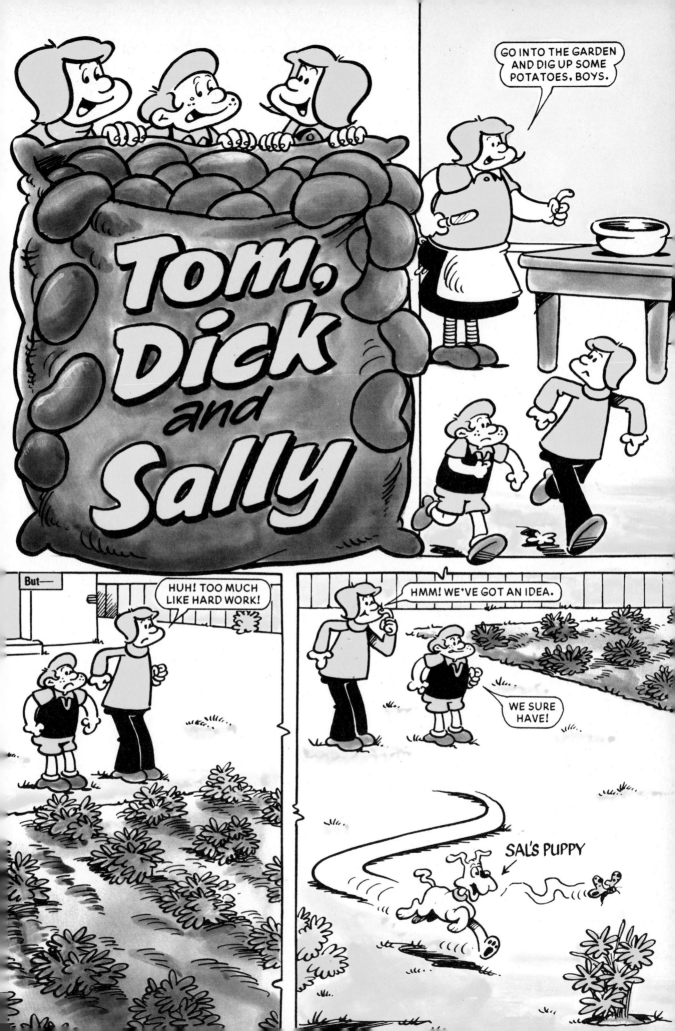

Help will come from a four-footed chum!

A mighty pick by Tom and Dick!

Don't fuss over a missed bus!

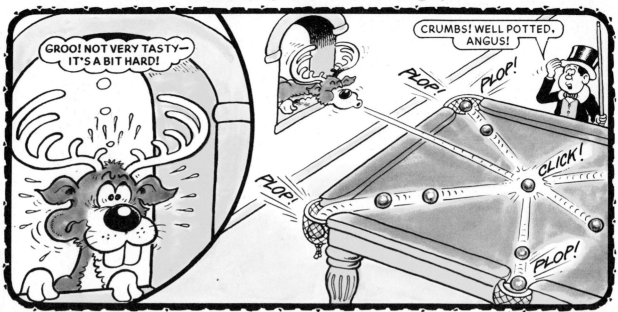

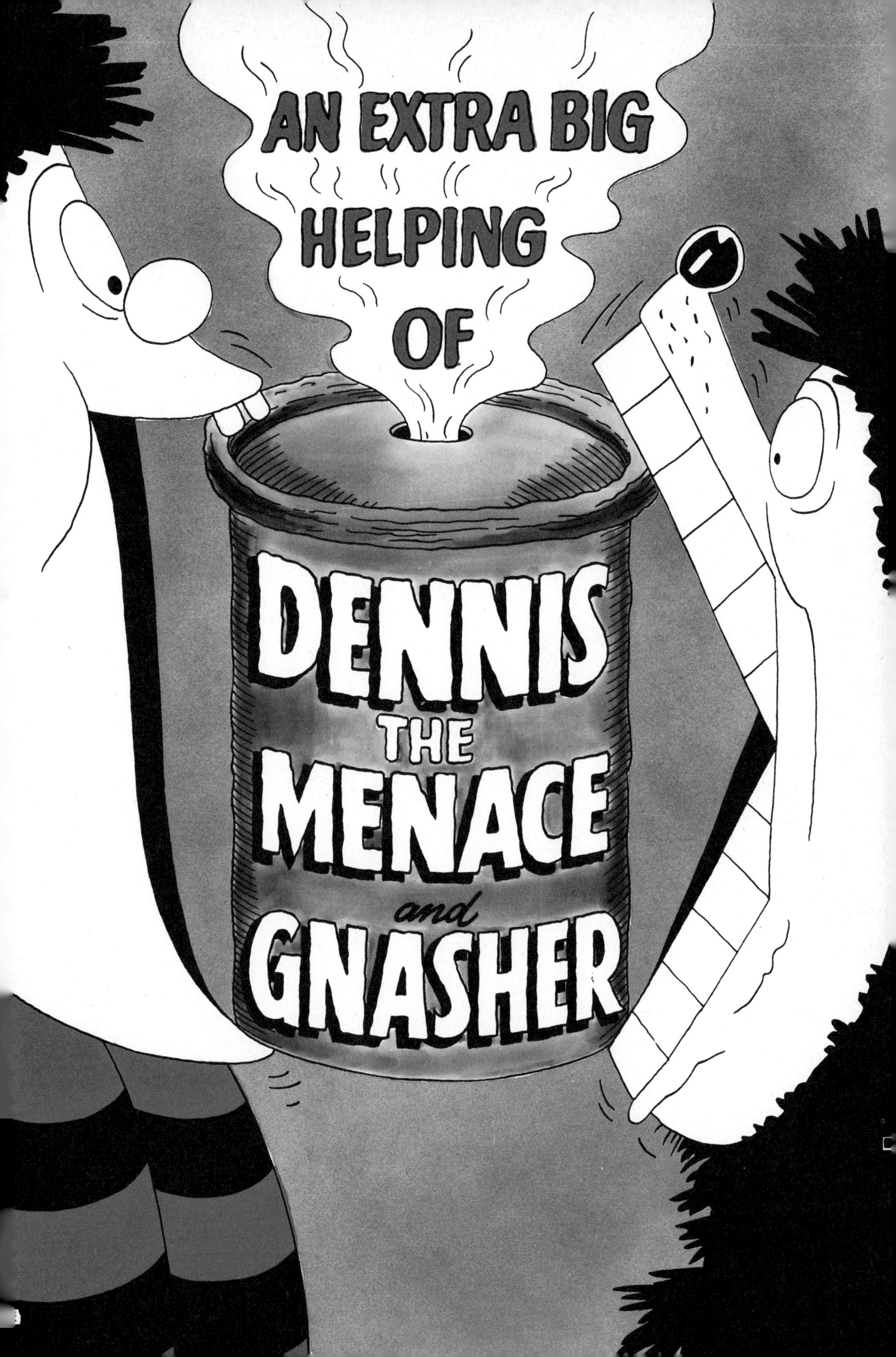
AN EXTRA BIG
HELPING
OF
DENNIS
THE
MENACE
and
GNASHER

BIRTHDAY Present

It's Dad's birthday—

WELL, I'VE HAD ALL MY PRESENTS EXCEPT YOURS, DENNIS.

CUPBOARD

I'LL GET IT RIGHT NOW, DAD.

OH-OH!

HANG ON!

EXCUSE ME JUST A SECOND, DAD!

EEK!

Curtain falls—Dad bawls!

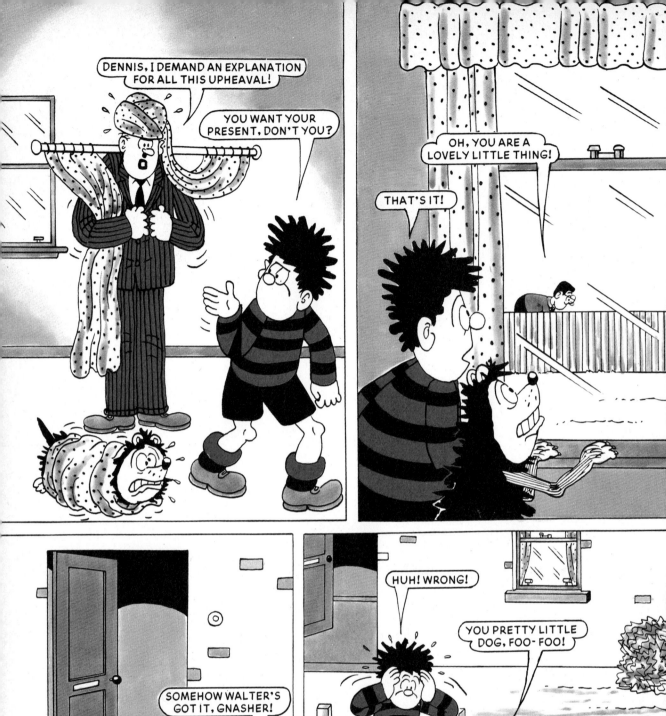

Mystery Story?

OUCH!

LET'S SEE IF THERE'S ANYTHING TO DO IN HERE, GNASHER.

GARDEN FETE

AUNT SALLY

FIND THE NEEDLE IN THE HAYSTACK 10p FOR TWO MINUTES

THAT'S DIFFERENT— I'LL HAVE A GO!

BET WE FIND THE NEEDLE BEFORE YOU DO, DENNIS.

TICKLE

ACHOO! ACHOO! ACHOO!

OO! NASTY GERMS!

THAT'S IT, DENNIS—YOUR TWO MINUTES ARE UP!

HEY, BUT WHAT ABOUT THE SOFTIES?

OH, WE PAID FOR AN HOUR!

A cunning act that's sure to attract!

Ball Boy does his bit—with a First Aid kit!

BALL BOY

WANT TO PLAY "HOSPITALS", BALL BOY?

BALL BOY'S COUSIN

NO CHANCE—I'M OFF TO PLAY FOOTBALL.

DRESSING ROOM

SQUEAK!

CREAK!

PUFF! THIS DOOR'S GETTING VERY STIFF.

SLAP!

THIS OINTMENT HELPED ME WHEN I HAD A STIFF KNEE.

FIRST AID

For goodness sake—a nasty break!

Gosh! I say! B.B. can't play!

By gum—startled Mum!

Quick trick!

"Game for

Spaghetti eating—painful meeting!

Bones needs to find some leads!

COO! IT'S THE BASH STREET PIGEONS

OWNED BY JANITOR

Look at that big scout hat!

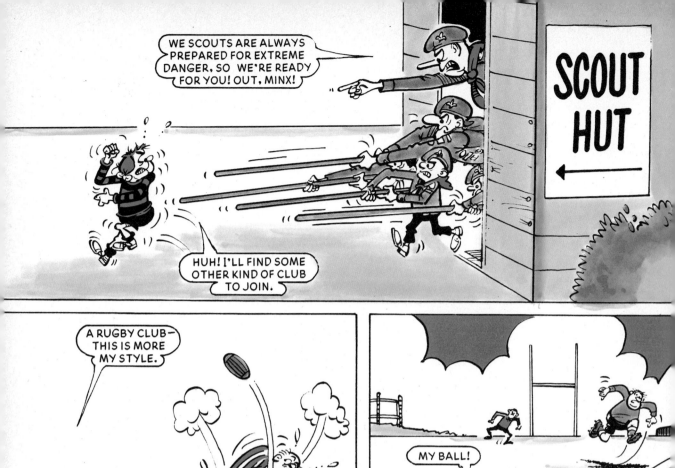

This club's for you, and Minnie, too!

IN ADDITION TO THESE SUPER BADGES YOU GET A SMART CLUB WALLET AND CLUB SECRETS **ALSO**

THERE'S A CHANCE TO WIN A SPECIAL DENNIS AND GNASHER T-SHIRT AND A DENNIS JERSEY EVERY WEEK! FULL DETAILS ABOUT HOW TO JOIN "DENNIS'S FAN CLUB" IN YOUR WEEKLY "BEANO".

What makes

a minx? *IF YOU DON'T KNOW— THEN LOOK BELOW!*

SOPPY TEA-PARTIES ARE NOT FOR MIN...

...JUST GIVE HER A NICE HOT CURRY!

MINNIE LOATHES BEING A BRIDESMAID...

...BUT SHE LIKES THROWING RICE— IN TINS, OF COURSE!

SHE HATES MUM'S ROCK-CAKES...

CRUNCH!

CORRECTION! SHE LOVES MUM'S ROCK-CAKES!

PYOING!

Yes, indeed, a messy feed!

IN THE ARMY

MUM'S SPIN-DRIER ISN'T HALF AS GOOD AS THIS!

Photo M.O.D.

Grandpa

AHA! THINK I'LL BECOME A WRITER!

FAMOUS WRITER KNIGHTED

So—

OLD FRED BORROWED MY TYPEWRITER A WHILE AGO—TO TYPE A LETTER TO QUEEN VICTORIA! CHUCKLE!

At Fred's house—

OF COURSE YOU CAN HAVE IT BACK— THERE IT IS—AT THE BOTTOM OF THAT PILE.

GNASHER'S TALE

MAKE A MENACE

A MOVING MODEL DENNIS FOR YOU TO CONSTRUCT

1. Draw a half-circle this size on a piece of card and cut out (you can trace the one shown here).
2. Paste the half-circle as shown and form into a cone.
3. Place the cone on another piece of card and draw a dotted line round its base.
4. Draw a larger circle and a smaller one as in the sketch.
5. Draw " V's " as shown and cut out shaded part.
6. Put a marble inside the cone, turn up the tabs on the base and paste them to the inside of the cone.
7. Trace the Dennis head and arms on to thick paper, cut out, colour and stick in position.

PASTE HERE

NOW GIVE DENNIS A PUSH AND WATCH HIM MOVE!

(Idea sent in by   Barry J. Coyne, Dundee.)

THE BASH STREET KIDS

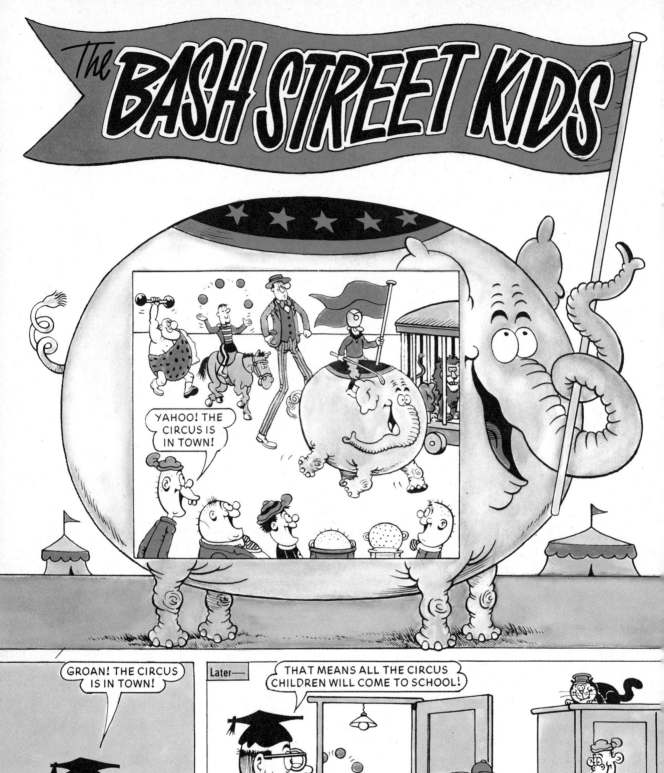

YAHOO! THE CIRCUS IS IN TOWN!

GROAN! THE CIRCUS IS IN TOWN!

Later—

THAT MEANS ALL THE CIRCUS CHILDREN WILL COME TO SCHOOL!

PLAYING FIELDS →

I'M GOING TO TRY TO ARRANGE A MATCH FOR TODAY, READERS.

HOPE YOU SCORE A TRY, BALL BOY.

A TRY? A TRY? THAT'S RUGBY! DO YOU GIRLS KNOW NOTHING ABOUT FOOTBALL?

TURN OVER TO SEE THE "GIRLS' GUIDE TO FOOTBALL" I'M WRITING, READERS!

This pretty field is a football pitch, where matches are played.

In amongst these lovely flowers we see a nice football. This is quite important to the game.

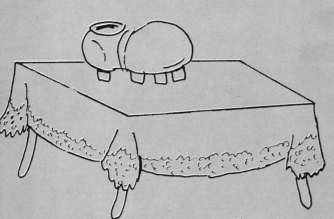

You put this football boot on your foot-this saves your toes getting hurt when you kick the ball.

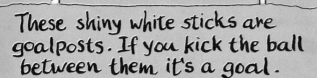

These shiny white sticks are goalposts. If you kick the ball between them it's a goal.

This nice man blows his whistle to start the game. His decisions are always right and everyone likes him.

The team with most goals wins. Both teams have a nice cup of tea and a chat after the game.

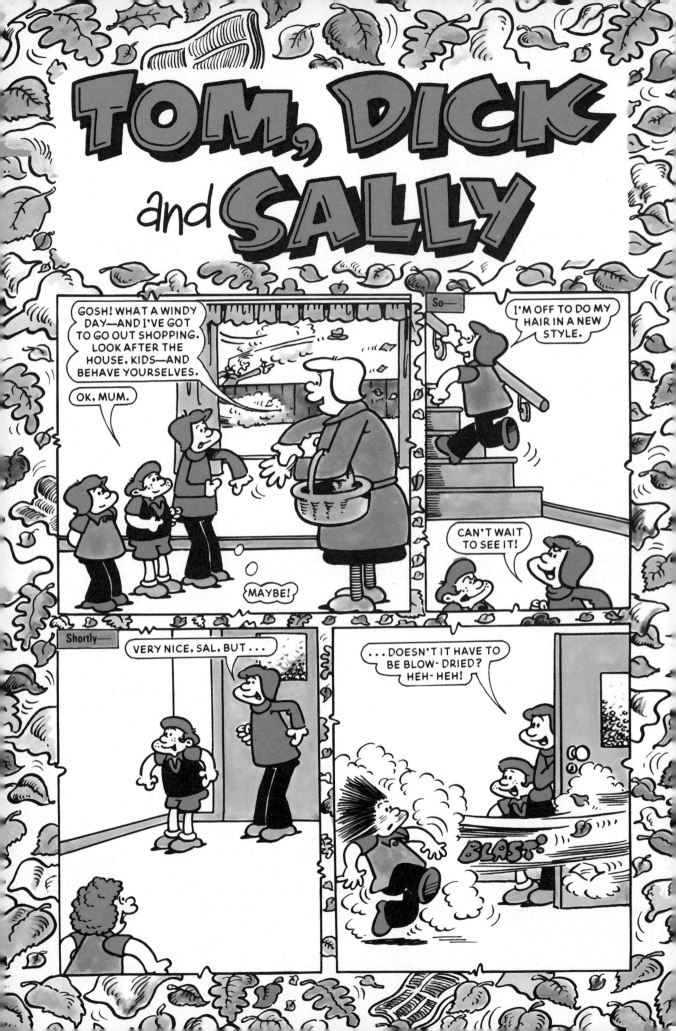

JUST WATCH!

NOW THE CAR'S STUCK IN THE MUD AND . . .

STUCK

. . .WE CAN PINCH THE GRUB! GOOD OLD PA!

But—

UGH!

MAYBE IF I TRY A BIT MORE POWER! . . .

One clean-up later—

I'M GOING TO PRETEND TO BE A PARK WARDEN. I'LL STOP THE CARS AND WARN THEM ABOUT THIEVING BEARS...

...WHILE WE LEAP OUT AND GRAB THE GRUB!

In the car—

VERY KIND OF YOU TO LET ME DRIVE YOUR CAR, WILLIAM, BUT I REALLY THINK YOU SHOULD HAVE TOLD ME WHERE THE BRAKES WERE!

THERE'S A PARK WARDEN AHEAD!

Little Plum

SNARL!

EEK! UM ATTACK BY OUR WORST ENEMIES, UM PUTTYFEET TRIBE!

After um attack—

CLEAR ALL THESE PUTTYFOOT WEAPONS AWAY, PLUM.

HUH!

BETTER MAKE A START...

RAIN BARREL

PULL

OOPS!

WHOOSH!

GLUB! SHOULD HAVE LEFT UM ARROW IN—PESKY PLUM!

Later—

I'LL ADD UM SPEAR TO UM PILE...

Plum's away without delay!

SMOKE CLOUDS, WHEN I BURN THESE DODGE BOOKS!

NO, DAD! DON'T DO IT, I BEG YOU!

WELL, IF YOU GO TO AUNT PRISCILLA'S WITHOUT ANY MORE BOTHER . . .

IT'S A DEAL! ANYTHING TO SAVE MY BELOVED DODGE BOOKS!

ROGER'S ON HIS WAY, READERS— YOU CAN'T SEE HIM FOR THAT **CLOUD OF DUST!**

ZOOM!

Whoever you are...

...NEVER BE WITHOUT

Wherever you are...

A "BEANO"!

OUT EVERY WEDNESDAY